Supermarket Soup

By Pamela Chan

ISBN: 978-1-338-88856-0

Editor: Liza Charlesworth
Art Director: Tannaz Fassihi; Designer: Tanya Chernyak
Photos ©: cover: Africa Studio/Shutterstock.com; 6: mohd kamarul hafiz/Shutterstock.com.
All other photos © Getty Images.

Printed in Jiaxing, China. First printing, January 2023.

SCHOLASTIC INC.

I help get the carrots.
Mmm, mmm, carrots!

I help get the celery.
Mmm, mmm, celery!

I help get the tomatoes.
Mmm, mmm, tomatoes!

I help get the potatoes.
Mmm, mmm, potatoes!

I help get the corn.
Mmm, mmm, corn!

I help get the noodles.
Mmm, mmm, noodles!

I help eat the soup.
Mmm, mmm, soup!